GCSE WJEC English
The Workbook
Reading Non-Fiction and Media Texts

This book is for anyone doing **GCSE WJEC English** at foundation level.

It contains lots of **tricky questions** designed to hone your **reading skills** — because that's the only way you'll get any **better**.

It's also got some daft bits in to try and make the whole experience at least vaguely entertaining for you.

What CGP is all about

Our sole aim here at CGP is to produce the highest quality books — carefully written, immaculately presented and dangerously close to being funny.

Then we work our socks off to get them out to you — at the cheapest possible prices.

CONTENTS

Section Five — Exam Techniques

Section Six — Sample Exam

Section Seven — Practice Exam

Published by Coordination Group Publications Ltd.

Editors:
Charley Darbishire
Thomas Harte
Kate Houghton
Katherine Reed
Edward Robinson
Rachel Selway
Jennifer Underwood
Laurence Stamford

Contributors:
John Bowyer
Roland Haynes

Acknowledgements:
The publisher would like to thank the following copyright holders for permission to reproduce texts and images.

Marc Leverton / The Big Issue
'The Recipe for Success' article reproduced with kind permission of Marc Leverton, The Big Issue, South West

Madhur Jaffrey
Extract from 'Climbing the Mango Trees'. Copyright © Madhur Jaffrey 2003. Reproduced by permission of the author c/o Rogers, Coleridge & White Ltd., 20 Powis Mews, London W11 1JN

BBC
'The joy of greyhound ownership' by Jenny Matthews. Abridged version of original story from BBC News
http://news.bbc.co.uk/1/hi/uk/5190992.stm

The Retired Greyhound Trust
'Volunteering can benefit dogs and you' © The Retired Greyhound Trust

Every effort has been made to locate copyright holders and obtain permission to reproduce texts and images.
For those texts and images where it has been difficult to trace the originator of the work, we would be
grateful for information. If any copyright holder would like us to make an amendment to the
acknowledgements, please notify us and we will gladly update the book at the next reprint. Thank you.

ISBN: 978 1 84762 106 1

With thanks to Paula Barnett, Julia Murphy and Jennifer Underwood for the proofreading.
With thanks to Laura Phillips for the copyright research.

Groovy website: www.cgpbooks.co.uk

Jolly bits of clipart from CorelDRAW®

Printed by Elanders Hindson Ltd, Newcastle upon Tyne.

The Audience

Q1   Circle the word which best describes the audience each sentence is aimed at.
The first one has been done for you.

a)   "Do you long for a simpler, more reliable way of managing
your finances?"   children / (adults)

b)   "When you play netball, first of all you have to decide which
position you would like to play."   experts / beginners

c)   "No trip to China is complete without seeing the famous and
fabulous Great Wall."   tourists / business people

Q2   What sort of people would you expect to read these publications?

a)   *The Rough Guide to Turkey*   ....

b)   *The Times Educational Supplement*   ....

c)   *The Big Book of Car Games*   ....

Q3   Read the text below and answer the question underneath.   MINI-ESSAY QUESTION

Are you looking for a cool summer job?

We've got loads of temporary vacancies with no experience required!

All you need is some free time, a positive attitude and plenty of energy. If you've got your own wheels that's even better!

Pickers... packers... stackers... waiters... waitresses... and TONS of others!

With Spondon Summer Jobs you can:
• gain great work experience
• make a few quid
• make new friends

Whatever you fancy, we can sort you out with a job that suits you down to the ground.
Interested? Call Jackie on 0547 262 626.

How does the advert aim to appeal to a teenage audience?

Write about:
• the language used
• the content of the advert
• the font styles and presentation used

You'll need to use a separate sheet of paper to answer the mini-essay questions.

The Purpose of the Text

Q1   Draw lines to match each type of text to its main purpose.

a)   "Who could disagree with the fact that children should eat healthily? Child obesity is on the rise — and we need to stop it."   **to entertain**

b)   "As the train moved south, first crawling, then increasing to a steady gallop, the scenery gradually changed from the flat and dull to the dramatic and beautiful."   **to inform**

c)   "Shop around for the best quote — some insurers are much more expensive than others."   **to persuade**

d)   "Tomorrow, there will be scattered showers in the north-west."   **to advise**

Q2   Put each of the following types of text into the correct column in the table, based on its main purpose. The first one has been done for you. You may find that some of these fit into more than one column.

a charity advertisement   a film review

a cake recipe   an agony aunt column in a magazine

a leaflet from a political party   an instruction manual for a computer

a cartoon in a newspaper   a leaflet with tips on how to give up smoking

an article about the Industrial Revolution

Texts that inform	Texts that entertain	Texts that argue or persuade	Texts that advise
		a charity advertisement	

Make 'em laugh, make 'em cry...

Authors don't just write the first thing that comes into their heads. They've usually got a purpose in mind — and they try to write in a way which helps them to achieve it.

Texts that Persuade or Argue

Q1   Draw lines to match each statement below to its purpose.

a)   "If you want to make a difference, there are many organisations you can join."

to persuade

b)   "By joining our march and signing this petition, you will be helping to put an end to this disgraceful act of cruelty."

to advise

Q2   Read the extract below, then circle whether you think its purpose is to argue or to persuade, and briefly explain your answer.

> The bad language used by youngsters today is disgraceful. What's more, they seem to have no respect for authority, and society is a worse place as a result.

I think the purpose is to **argue / persuade**.

Explanation ....

....

....

Q3   Read the extract from a leaflet below and then answer the question about it underneath.

Come to Rufford Aquarium — you'll have a whale of a time!

Rufford Aquarium is the only place in the county where you can see local and exotic species of fish and sea mammals all in one place.

Experience the magic of the deep as you are surrounded by the underwater world. You could be eyed up by an octopus, shaken by a shark or peered at by pike!

Whatever your age, you're guaranteed a fantastic time.

Entry costs: Adult — £6   Child — £3   Family ticket — £15

Rufford Aquarium — a great family day out!

How does the presentation and choice of language persuade the reader to visit the aquarium?
Write about:
• font size and style
• language techniques (e.g. rule of three, alliteration, puns)

Texts that Inform, Entertain or Advise

Q1   Circle the word that best describes the purpose of the text below.

> A stern telling-off after bad behaviour is often all that is needed to ensure your child grows into a responsible, considerate individual.

Is that all I'm here for — your entertainment?

advise   entertain

Q2   From the text below, pick out a word or phrase that advises and a word or phrase that entertains.

> Thai food can be startlingly hot, so watch out! The chefs round here get through chillies like you wouldn't believe — though some relief comes from the creamy coconut milk that tames the fire of the burning hot curries. For the more adventurous, the colourful cuisine of the north-east is worth trying. Generous use of lime juice, garlic and fish gives it a distinctive aroma.

a)   Advises: ....

b)   Entertains: ....

Q3   Read the two texts below, then say which text is informative and which text is entertaining. Write a brief explanation for each answer.

a)
> The Battle of Hastings was fought on October 14th 1066 on a field near Hastings in East Sussex. Led by William the Conqueror, it was the Normans' most important victory over the Anglo-Saxons, commanded by King Harold II, in their invasion of England.

This text is **entertaining / informative** because ....

....

....

b)
> The battle was furious and bloody, and vast numbers of soldiers were brutally slain. At one stage the English were fooled into thinking they had won the battle, and stormed towards their enemy, only to find themselves ambushed and mercilessly slaughtered.

This text is **entertaining / informative** because ....

....

....

Formal Style and Informal Style

Q1   For each pair of sentences, underline the more formal sentence.

a)   "Sorry! We don't take credit cards."
       "Customers are advised that we do not accept credit cards."

b)   "It is essential to ensure you have the correct tools before proceeding."
       "Check you've got the proper kit to hand before you go any further."

Q2   Put each language feature in the correct column, based on where you would usually expect to find it.

non-standard English		Formal texts	Informal texts
standard English			
complex sentences			
simple sentences			
chatty tone			
serious tone			
contractions (e.g. "don't")			
impersonal style			
personal style			
humour			

Q3   The text below is taken from a travel journal. Is the style of the text formal or informal?
       Write down two pieces of evidence from the text that back up your answer.

> At this point on my train journey I was starting to get a tad — how shall I put it? — narked off.
> It's one thing being patient, accepting the fact that things don't always go to plan and that now
> and then delays just happen. It's quite another to be told, after paying good money for a ticket
> on the grounds that it's taking you to Town A, that apparently for no good reason we're taking a
> little detour through Village B, River C and Swamp D.

The style is **informal / formal** because:

1) ....

2) ....

I like your style...

The style a writer chooses has to be right for the audience. If you can work out who the audience
is, it will help you understand <u>why</u> the writer has chosen to write in a particular <u>style</u>.

Personal Tone and Impersonal Tone

Q1   Write a **P** for "personal" or an **I** for "impersonal" to describe the tone that would usually be created by each of these techniques.

a) written in first person ("I")   ☐   d) lots of facts used   ☐

b) lots of opinions   ☐   e) sounds emotional   ☐

c) formal language used   ☐   f) slang used   ☐

Q2   Decide whether the text below has a personal or an impersonal tone. Find two pieces of evidence from the text to support your answer.

> There is a growing feeling that the situation concerning air pollution needs to be addressed. The number of individuals suffering from breathing problems in the city has been steadily increasing for years, with levels of dust particles and nitrogen oxides soaring to new heights. Possible solutions are to be discussed at the next city council meeting.

The tone is **personal / impersonal** because:

1) ....

2) ....

Q3   Read the following extract from an agony aunt column and then answer the question at the bottom of the page.

MINI-ESSAY QUESTION

> Dear Fiona,
>
> You poor thing, you're really down in the dumps, aren't you? I know it's hard to believe but your life will improve — you just need to take control over things again. Concentrate on what you used to be like, when you were more confident and enjoying life.
>
> One thing that's definitely worth a shot is consulting a career guidance counsellor. If you haven't got time for this then there are plenty of books that I can recommend on choosing the right job.
>
> The main thing to remember is that you're the boss of your own life — so take charge!

What techniques does the writer use to create a friendly, personal style in her writing?

Following an Argument

Q1 Writers use many different techniques when they argue a point.
Draw a line to match each of the following techniques with the correct example.

fact	"I strongly believe that we can win the World Cup."
opinion	"Surely you don't believe these disgusting lies?"
implication	"For example, a right angle is 90°."
rhetorical question	"Ever since Mr Hardcastle resigned, Mrs Hardy has been in a good mood."

implication = suggesting something without saying it directly

rhetorical question = a question to which an answer isn't expected

Q2 The text below is a letter printed by the Daily Duncaster local newspaper.
Read the text, and then answer the questions that follow.

Dear Sir,

I was horrified to read your article about the new soft drink "Swampy Water" being served in the tuck shop at Duncaster Primary School. This dangerous fad for drinking green, gungy water is clearly idiotic. Firstly, young children might get confused and think it's all right to drink *real* swamp water. I know from my time in the Territorial Army that this can make you very ill indeed. Secondly, "Swampy Water" is full of unhealthy sugar and additives — how else could it be that bright green colour? Last but not least, the drink is expensive and means children don't have money left over to buy normal, healthy snacks. To conclude, "Swampy Water" should be removed from the tuck shop at Duncaster Primary School immediately.

Yours faithfully,
Gerry Bowness

a) What is the **main** argument of the letter? Tick the correct option below.

☐ Drinking swamp water can make you ill.

☐ "Swampy Water" is unhealthy because it contains additives and sugar.

☐ "Swampy Water" shouldn't be on sale in Duncaster Primary School.

Driver, follow that argument...

b) Write down three points the writer makes to support his argument.
Write them using your own words.

1. ....

2. ....

3. ....

Evaluating an Argument

Q1　Which of the following would be **bad** to use in an argument? Tick the correct answers.

- [ ] inconsistencies
- [ ] formal tone
- [ ] out-of-date examples
- [ ] confusing explanations
- [ ] irony
- [ ] factual inaccuracies
- [ ] points backed up with examples
- [ ] persuasive language techniques

Driver, evaluate
that argument...

What?

Q2　Read the following texts. Describe one good
point and one bad point about each argument.

a)
> The greatest television presenter of all time is Terry Wogan. When he first appeared on television
> in 1865, Wogan astonished everyone with his energy, enthusiasm and sparkling wit. He had a star
> quality which all previous television presenters lacked. Who could fail to be charmed by him?

A **good** point about this argument is ....

....

A **bad** point about this argument is ....

....

b)
> As archaeologist David Field says: "There is debate about what ancient stone circles were used for.
> However, it is almost certain that they had some religious significance." There is strong evidence that many
> stone circles were religious sites. For example, human and animal bones have been found at Stonehenge.
> This suggests religious ceremonies were carried out at the site. The evidence is quite weak though.

A **good** point about this argument is ....

....

A **bad** point about this argument is ....

....

Not bad, shame about the ranting...

When evaluating an argument, try to think of good and bad points about it. It's important to back
up your points with examples though. Just saying, "this argument is rubbish," won't do.

Evaluating an Argument

Q1   Read the following text then answer the question that follows.

> I love the colour pink. I love birds. I really love flamingos. How could anyone dislike them?
> They're the most fascinating, mysterious and beautiful birds in the world! That's why I'm
> starting a campaign to persuade people to sponsor flamingos in zoos. By donating a few
> pounds, people can help fund the setting up of breeding programmes for rare flamingo species.
> The head keeper at my local zoo, Jane Sutton says, "Flamingos really are wonderful creatures.
> Any donations would be much appreciated."

The table below shows the techniques used by the writer.
Fill in the table by picking out examples of each technique.

Technique	Example from text
repetition of words / phrases	
rhetorical question	
expert opinion	
exaggeration	

Q2   Read the notice below and answer the question underneath.

Volunteers Needed for Salem Street Neighbourhood Group

No one wants to find litter and dog dirt on the pavement outside the front door. No one wants to have
graffiti scratched on the car. No one wants to be woken up in the middle of the night by loud music or
people arguing in the street. But, sadly, these things happen all the time in Salem Street. We all deserve
to live in a **pleasant, safe, clean** street. And if we join together **we can make it happen**.

- A committee of Salem Street residents is being formed to look at issues like anti-social behaviour, litter and noise
  levels. It's an opportunity for **us**, the people who live in Salem Street, to be proactive and **improve our community**.

- Similar street committees in the Runford area have proved **very effective** in reducing anti-social behaviour, e.g.
  Midden Avenue, which used to suffer from high levels of litter and graffiti, is now a very clean, pleasant street.

- Helping with the committee won't take up much of your time — but it will make a **big difference** to Salem Street.
  Come along and find out more about the committee at our first meeting in **Rixy's Bingo Hall, 8pm, 16th May**.

How well does this notice persuade the reader to join the committee?
Write about:

- examples the writer uses to persuade the reader
- language devices the writer uses

Facts and Opinions

Q1   Write down whether the following statements are opinions, facts or false facts.

a)   London is the capital city of the UK.

....

b)   Glasgow would be a better capital city of Scotland than Edinburgh.

....

c)   Manchester is the capital city of England.

....

d)   I think that snowboarding is overrated.

....

e)   Most pupils take their GCSE exams in Year 11.

....

Q2   Read the statements below. For each one, say whether you think it is a fact or an opinion and explain your choice.

It's not always clear if something is a fact or an opinion — you have to work it out for yourself.

a)   "Water boils at 100 degrees Celsius."

....

....

b)   "As Madonna gets older, her music gets better."

....

....

Q3   Read the advert below and answer the question that follows.

Superspeedade — the best sports drink on the market

Superspeedade is the unbeatable new sports drink from *Food Drink PLC*. It's jam-packed with all the nutrition you need to excel at sport. For example, it has a high carbohydrate content which is a good source of energy. It also contains the vitamins riboflavin and niacin, which help with the release of energy from carbohydrates.

It gives you the energy you need for sporting success

Explain how the writer uses **facts** in this advert to persuade the reader to buy the drink.

....

....

....

....

....

Facts and Opinions

Q1 Read the text below. It was taken from a newspaper article.
After you've read it, answer the questions below.

We're All Getting Older
Edward Lightburn

From The Daily Splurge, Thursday 2ⁿᵈ March 2006

We're all living longer and longer. In 1900 in the USA, people could expect to live to around 47 years of age. In 2000 life expectancy had risen to 77 years and the trend is continuing. It might not be long until most people live until they're in their nineties, or even over one hundred.

What are we all going to be doing when we're eighty-something? At the moment, old people don't really get a good deal. As soon as they're too troublesome for their families, they get booted out of home and shipped off to the nearest "care home". At these places, they'll be patronised, prodded and poked like sick animals: "Does Sarah want her din-dins now? It's her favourite..." It's not something to look forward to, is it?

It used to be that the elderly were respected for their wisdom. Now they're treated like the waste product of society, thrown out and left to rot in their care homes, the landfill sites of modern humanity.

a) Write down two facts and two opinions from the text.

Facts:

1. ....

2. ....

Opinions:

1. ....

2. ....

Well, I wanted to do something special for your 130th...

BINGO

b) What do you think the writer's attitude to old people is?
Use evidence from the text to back up your answer.

....

....

....

....

....

False facts — also known as "fibs"...

It can be tricky to tell the difference between facts and opinions. It's a skill you need to practise though, or you'll have difficulty working out exactly what a writer is trying to argue.

Rhetoric and Bias

Q1   Draw lines to match up each persuasive technique to the example which uses it.

a)   **rhetorical question**   i)   Nothing is more disgusting than a mouldy sandwich.

b)   **repetition of words/phrases**   ii)   Who on earth would want to eat a mouldy sandwich?

c)   **exaggeration**   iii)   I hate mould. I hate sandwiches. I really hate mouldy sandwiches.

Q2   Decide whether the following texts are biased or unbiased. Explain your answers.

a)    By far the best hobby for young people is the card game "cribbage". All young people from the ages of eight to eighteen adore playing cribbage. It's easy to learn, doesn't need much equipment and provides hours of fun.

Bias = when the writer's personal opinions affect what he or she writes.

I think the text is **biased / unbiased** because ....

....

....

b)   In Orkney, you can visit the remains of a Neolithic (Stone Age) village called Skara Brae. The village was inhabited about 5000 years ago. You can see the remains of walls, doorways, fireplaces and stone "furniture".

I think the text is **biased / unbiased** because ....

....

....

Q3   Read this extract from a travel brochure and answer the question that follows.   MINI-ESSAY QUESTION

Malliwest Resort Hotels

Everyone daydreams. When you're stuck in the office — dealing with tricky customers, struggling with spreadsheets, drinking tepid tea — can you honestly say you haven't dreamt of lying on a sunny beach in a luxury resort, sipping cocktails and being waited on hand and foot?

At Malliwest Resorts you can make your dreams a reality. Only at Malliwest Resorts can you reserve a private beach so that no one else can see what you look like in your swimming costume. Only at Malliwest Resorts can you order your favourite meal and have it made specially. Only at Malliwest Resorts can you ring room service at 4am and get a polite response!

Malliwest Resorts' top priority is to make sure you have the **holiday of a lifetime**. If you book before 20th June, you'll get 15% off the price of your holiday. Surely this is an offer to fulfil anyone's dreams?

How does the writer use language techniques to persuade the reader to visit Malliwest hotels?

Headlines and Subheadings

Q1 Draw lines to connect 'headline' and 'subheading' with the descriptions on the right that apply to them. Some descriptions may apply to both.

headline

larger than the main text

at the top of the page

used to split up a story

subheading

used to grab attention

Q2 For each of the following headlines, write down **one** language device which makes it effective. Write a brief explanation of how each language device works.

a)
Ray runs riot in
Sheldon showdown

....

....

b)
New Italian restaurant
offers a pizza the action

....

....

c)
Outrage at massive
tax increase

....

....

Graphics and Captions

Q1   Briefly explain the intended purpose of each graphic and its caption.

a)   (from a newspaper article
       about population growth)

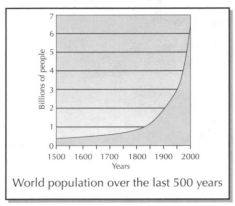

World population over the last 500 years

b)   (from a hotel brochure)

All our rooms are clean,
comfortable and luxurious

a) **Purpose of the population graph and caption**

....

....

....

b) **Purpose of the hotel photo and caption**

....

....

....

Q2   Read the following advertisement for the holiday destination of Montserrat.
       How do the headings, photographs and captions help to achieve the text's purpose?

MINI-ESSAY
QUESTION

MONTSERRAT

The Emerald Isle of the Caribbean

Montserrat is a beautiful, lush, green, mountainous island, which Irish
settlers named "the Emerald Isle of the Caribbean". Montserrat lies 27
miles south-west of Antigua, in the Eastern Caribbean chain of islands.

Relax on the island's idyllic,
secluded beaches

Learn to dive amid beautiful
unspoilt coral reefs

The beaches in Montserrat are remarkable in appearance as they have
glistening black sand because of the volcanic nature of the island.
They are some of the most secluded and unspoilt beaches in the world.
For swimming and sunbathing they provide the most calming and
leisurely experience available. The beaches also provide incomparable
surroundings for diving, snorkelling and other water sports.

Text Boxes and Columns

Q1   How do the columns add to the effectiveness of the following text?

Parrots under threat from pet trade

A British-based conservation organisation has warned that the future of the world's parrots is severely threatened by the international trade for pets.

Thousands of parrots are captured and brought to Europe and North America each year, with many dying during the journey. Neotropical parrots have become one of the most threatened groups of birds in the world, because of international trade and also deforestation of their natural habitats.

This trend is all the more alarming, the organisation says, because until recently parrots have flourished, with numbers on the increase.

....

....

....

Q2   Explain why you think text boxes have been used in the following examples.

a)

*Energise, revitalise and relax...
...and work off those extra pounds!*

Bring this document to our reception to claim your free 2-week trial voucher (valid until the end of December). You will be entitled to free gym and pool use, exercise classes, social events and loads more!

....

....

b)

Here are just two examples of children who have benefited from the generosity of people like you:

Name: Oscar Luis
Age: 9
Story: Oscar used to live in a tin hut in the *barrios* of São Paulo. He now has clean water and basic medical services.

Name: Srinitha
Age: 7
Story: Tiny Srinitha used to beg in the train stations of Delhi. Now she lives in a modest but safe apartment with her foster parents.

....

....

Don't text "columns" and "box" to the examiner...

When you write about layout features like text columns and text boxes, it's not enough just to point them out. You have to explain why the writer has used them and why they are effective.

Bullet Points and Numbered Lists

Q1   Explain why the use of bullet points or numbered lists is effective in the following texts.

a)

Flu strikes hard and fast. Symptoms may include:

- fever
- aching all over the body
- headache
- dry cough
- lack of appetite
- extreme tiredness

Do I look like I want to write about bullet points?

....
....
....
....

b)

Chocolate cake recipe:

1) Lightly grease and line two 20cm wide, 4cm deep sandwich tins.
2) Pre-heat the oven to 180°C / gas mark 4.
3) Beat together the butter, sugar, eggs, flour, baking powder and cocoa.
4) Divide the mixture evenly between the prepared tins.
5) Bake for about 25 minutes, until risen and rich, dark brown.

....
....
....
....

"Interesting" is boring...

When you talk about presentational devices it's important you say __how__ they work. It's no good just saying that they make the text more interesting — you have to explain in more detail.

Font Styles and Formatting

Q1 What impression is created by the following fonts? Explain why you think each font has been used.

a) | Global warming is "worse than previously thought", say Antarctic scientists |

....

....

b) | **Looking for a great day of family fun? Give Franny's Fun Farm a ring!** |

....

....

c) | Sometimes you need to take a few risks — and don't underestimate your own abilities... |

....

....

Q2 Describe the effects of text formatting in the following extracts.

a)

the ... story ... day.
The failing company's chief
executive has awarded himself
a pay rise of a **whopping £50,000**!

Despit ... rsist ... mours ... bankru...

....

....

b)

Event: World Peace Rally
Date: 15th April
Time: 7.30pm
Place: Hartnell Square

Peace stinks! And so do you!
Aargh!!
Rambo for prime minister

....

....

Presentation and Layout — Overview

Q1   Read the text below and then answer the question at the bottom of the page.

Eat Superfoods to Give Your Health a Boost

Change your diet and feel better than ever — we tell you how...

By Tyler Steele

If your New Year's resolution to live more healthily hasn't taken off yet, don't panic — here are some of the top "superfoods", as recommended by dieticians:

• **Carrots** provide beta-carotene, which can reduce the risk of stroke.

• **Chilli peppers** can help to reduce cholesterol and protect you from cancer.

• **Tomatoes** stimulate immune functions.

• **Citrus fruits** are an excellent source of vitamin C, which helps your body fight cancers.

Health experts are keen to point out, though, that in addition to a balanced and nutritious diet, a healthy lifestyle must also include regular exercise. A good mixture of aerobic and anaerobic exercise taken three times a week is a good general guide.

"Exercise" doesn't have to mean getting up at 5a.m. every day and running a half marathon! Something as easy as a brisk 30 minute walk every day can make a big contribution to improved health.

Write down four presentational devices the writer uses in the leaflet and explain why they are effective.

1. ....
....
....

2. ....
....
....

3. ....
....
....

4. ....
....
....

Descriptive Language

Q1   Write down what the word "imagery" means.

....

....

Q2   Writers sometimes use the five senses (sight, touch, smell, sound and taste) to describe things. Circle which of the five senses is being used in each of the following descriptions.

a) "They were drawn to the kitchen by the familiar, welcoming scent of freshly-baked bread."

sight   touch   smell   sound   taste

b) "The glass eye felt cold and smooth like a pebble."

sight   touch   smell   sound   taste

* Adjectives are describing words.

Q3   Underline the adjectives* in the following description.

> "I had five tedious hours to wait at Singapore's shiny, modern airport. While my bulging holdall rested at my tired, sandalled feet, I observed the curious surroundings. An interesting mix of travellers bustled by: excited families, overweight businessmen, dirty young backpackers. My nostrils detected the heavenly scent of fresh croissants and strong coffee wafting from the over-priced eateries. I felt a slight chill and dry mouth from the air conditioning, yet was grateful: better to be sitting in a fake, cool breeze than wilting outside under the burning sun."

Q4   Read the text below, then answer the questions in the lovely coloured boxes.

From *Memories of Aldport*, by Geoff Buckley

I visited the old, ghostly railway bridge down the road from where I grew up. The grey, rusty bridge sparked countless memories of days gone by — the thunderous roar of an approaching train echoing down the track like a warning of an alien invasion.

The fact that nothing passes under the bridge any more adds to the eerie atmosphere the station has now. I would like to take a stroll along the railway track's forbidding, overgrown lines — but the combination of the unnecessary barbed wire fence and the thick, thorny bushes which try to trip you up, sadly makes this impossible.

a) How does the writer of this text feel about the railway bridge he describes?

b) What writing techniques are used to describe the bridge and trains? What impression do they create?

Metaphors and Similes

Q1 Draw lines to link each term with its correct definition:

a) **metaphor**   A comparison where the writer says that something is something else.

b) **simile**   A comparison where the writer says something is similar to something else, often using the words "like" or "as".

Q2 For each phrase, say whether it is a metaphor or a simile.

a) John's as thick as two short planks.   ⟹ ....

b) Her eyes were X-rays, penetrating my soul.   ⟹ ....

c) Jane was a tower of strength.   ⟹ ....

d) I was stuck like a lettuce in a teapot.   ⟹ ....

Q3 What impression is created by the following simile?

When hunky Brad Depp walked into the room, Jane blushed as red as a beetroot.

....

....

....

Q4 What impression is created by the following metaphor?

Jane's heart was a block of ice which melted when she kissed hunky Brad Depp.

....

....

....

I know the writer quite well — I metaphor times...
Make sure you've got these terms worked out in your head before the exam. Metaphors and similes are similar but you need to learn the difference between them.

CGP

GCSE WJEC English

Reading Non-Fiction and Media Texts

Answer Book

Foundation Level

The Answers

Section One

Page 1 — The Audience

Q1 a) adults
b) beginners
c) tourists

Q2 a) • People who are about to visit Turkey.
• People deciding where to go on holiday.
b) • Teachers
• People with an interest in education.
c) • Children
• Parents taking children on car journeys.

Q3 Here are a few points you could write about:
The language used:
• Slang is used, e.g. "cool", "we can sort you out", to make it sound as if it's a young person talking to you.
• Informal words, e.g. "we've", "you've", give it an easy-going feel.
• Second person ("you") makes it sound chatty, friendly and direct.
The content of the advertisement:
• The nature of the work, e.g. "temporary" and "summer job" could appeal to teenagers looking for work in school / college holidays.
• The jobs do not require experience, which most young people do not have.
The font styles and presentation used:
• Font style is informal and friendly, suggesting the jobs will be fun — this will appeal to teenage readers.
• Short paragraphs, columns, bullet points and text boxes break the text up, making it easier to follow and therefore more appealing to a younger audience.

Page 2 — The Purpose of the Text

Q1 a) to persuade
b) to entertain
c) to advise
d) to inform

Q2 *Texts that inform:*
• a cake recipe
• an article about the Industrial Revolution
• a film review
• an instruction manual for a computer
Texts that entertain:
• a cartoon in a newspaper
• a film review
• an agony aunt column in a magazine
Texts that argue or persuade:
• a charity advertisement

• a leaflet from a political party
• a film review
Texts that advise:
• an agony aunt column in a magazine
• a leaflet with tips on how to give up smoking

Page 3 — Texts that Persuade or Argue

Q1 a) to advise
b) to persuade

Q2 *Purpose:* To argue
Explanation: • It expresses a strong viewpoint in an emotive way, but does not suggest that the reader should do anything.

Q3 Here are a few of the ideas you could develop for this answer:
Font size and style:
• Use of text formatting, such as bold and italics, makes key phrases stand out to persuade the reader, e.g. "a great family day out!"
• Informal, easy-to-read font emphasises the idea that the aquarium is family-oriented.
• Larger font used to make the statement "Rufford Aquarium — a great family day out!" stand out to the reader.
Language techniques:
• The pun "whale of a time" creates an impression of the aquarium being a fun place, attracting the reader.
• Alliteration, e.g. "peered at by pike", emphasises the variety of things to see and makes them sound exciting.
• Strong, positive adjectives, e.g. "fantastic", "great", make the tone of the text more persuasive.
• Rule of three used ("eyed up by an octopus, shaken by a shark or peered at by pike!") to emphasise the variety of species on display.

Page 4 — Texts that Inform, Entertain or Advise

Q1 advise

Q2 *Meant to advise:*
• watch out
• for the more adventurous
• distinctive aroma
Meant to entertain:
• startlingly
• like you wouldn't believe
• burning hot
• colourful cuisine

Q3 a) • This text is **informative** because it gives specific facts, such as the date and the leaders, and explains the importance of the battle.

b) • This text is **entertaining** because it uses strong, emotive adjectives such as "furious and bloody", and emphasises the violence to make the battle seem dramatic.

Page 5 — Formal Style and Informal Style

Q1 a) "Customers are advised that we do not accept credit cards."
b) "It is essential to ensure you have the correct tools before proceeding."

Q2 *Formal texts:* standard English, complex sentences, serious tone, impersonal style.
Informal texts: non-standard English, simple sentences, chatty tone, contractions, personal style, humour.

Q3 The style is **informal**.
Suggestions for reasons (you only need to write two):
• slang is used, e.g. "narked off"
• humour is used, e.g. "River C and Swamp D"
• contractions are used, e.g. "It's"
• some of it is written in a personal style, e.g. "I was starting to get..."

Page 6 — Personal Tone and Impersonal Tone

Q1 a) P
b) P
c) I
d) I
e) P
f) P

Q2 The tone is **impersonal** because:
• Opinions are given indirectly, e.g. "There is a growing feeling".
• Formal language is used, e.g. "individuals".

Q3 *Here are some points you could make:*
• The writer addresses the reader by her first name: "Dear Fiona", making it seem as if she knows her.
• The writer uses a chatty, informal tone, using slang such as "down in the dumps". This creates the impression of her being a friend giving advice.
• She uses positive words and phrases such as "you're the boss of your own life" to sound encouraging and helpful.
• She writes in the first person, e.g. "I know it's hard to believe..."

The Answers

Section Two

Page 7 — Following an Argument

Q1 **fact:** ""For example, a right angle is 90°."
opinion: "I strongly believe that we can win the World Cup."
implication: "Ever since Mr Hardcastle resigned, Mrs Hardy has been in a good mood."
rhetorical question: "Surely you don't believe these disgusting lies?"

Q2 a) "Swampy Water" shouldn't be on sale in Duncaster Primary School.

b) • Young children might get mixed up and drink real swamp water by mistake.

• The drink is bad for your health.

• The drink costs a lot of money.

Page 8 — Evaluating an Argument

Q1 The following should be ticked: inconsistencies, out-of-date examples, confusing explanations, factual inaccuracies

Q2 a) *Suggestions for good points:*
• The writer uses a rhetorical question, "Who could fail to be charmed by him?" to persuade the reader to agree with the argument.
• The writer uses strong statements, e.g. "Wogan astonished everyone". The confident tone of these statements makes the writer's argument more persuasive.
Suggestions for bad points:
• The writer doesn't back up the points with evidence. For example, when she says "He had a star quality", she doesn't give examples or quotes to back this up.
• The writer makes a factual inaccuracy when she says Wogan "first appeared on television in 1865" — television hadn't even been invented then.

b) *Suggestions for good points:*
• The writer uses a quote from an expert to back up his argument.
• The writer uses specific evidence about Stonehenge to back up his general point about stone circles.
Suggestions for bad points:
• The writer contradicts himself. He says that the evidence is "strong", and then later says the evidence is "weak".
• The writer seems to make some quite big assumptions, e.g. that finding "human and animal bones" definitely means that religious rituals were carried out.

Page 9 — Evaluating an Argument

Q1

Technique	Example from text
repetition of words / phrases	• "I love" repeated
rhetorical question	• "How could anyone dislike them?"
expert opinion	• Head keeper at zoo quoted
exaggeration	• "the most fascinating, mysterious and beautiful birds in the world!"

Q2 Here are a few points you could write for each bullet point:
Examples the writer uses to persuade the reader:
• The writer gives examples of how unpleasant the street is at the moment, e.g. litter and noise. This reminds readers of these bad things and might make them more likely to join the group.
• The writer gives an example of a similar community group which has improved the quality of another street. This might make readers think the group is likely to be effective.
• On the other hand, the writer doesn't give any examples of what the group will actually do to reduce anti-social behaviour.
Language devices the writer uses:
• The writer repeats the phrase "No one wants" three times which increases the impact of the opening statements.
• The writer uses positive, inclusive phrases like "we can make it happen" to make the reader feel involved and enthusiastic about the project.

Page 10 — Facts and Opinions

Q1 a) fact
b) opinion
c) false fact
d) opinion
e) fact

Q2 a) Fact:
• because it's been proven scientifically.
b) Opinion:
• because it's a matter of personal taste how good Madonna's music is.

Q3 • The writer uses facts to explain how the drink helps to provide energy, e.g. "it has a high carbohydrate content which is a good source of energy". This might help persuade the reader that the drink really would work and that the advert's claims are true.

Page 11 — Facts and Opinions

Q1 a) Facts:
• In 1900 in the USA, life expectancy was 47 years old.
• In 2000 in the USA, life expectancy was 77 years old.
Opinions:
• Old people aren't treated well nowadays, e.g. they're patronised and treated badly in care homes.
• Old people used to be treated with more respect.
b) • The writer seems to care about the elderly because he implies that they should be treated with more respect, e.g. he says that in the past they were treated with respect, but now they're "treated like the waste product of society".
• He thinks that old people deserve better because they "don't really get a good deal."

Page 12 — Rhetoric and Bias

Q1 a) ii)
b) iii)
c) i)

Q2 a) I think the text is **biased** because...
• it presents the opinion of the writer as fact, e.g. it claims that all young people "adore" playing cribbage which isn't true.
b) I think the text is **unbiased** because...
• it gives facts and figures about Skara Brae, e.g. it says the village was inhabited about 5000 years ago.

Q3 Here are some points you could make:
• The writer uses rhetorical questions to help persuade readers to visit the resorts, e.g. "Surely this is an offer to fulfil anyone's dreams?"
• The writer uses repetition to emphasise the unique qualities of the resorts. The phrase "Only at Malliwest Resorts can you" is repeated three times.
• The writer uses exaggeration to emphasise the quality of holidays provided by the resorts, for example using phrases like "holiday of a lifetime" and "make your dreams a reality".

The Answers

Section Three

Page 13 — Headlines and Subheadings

Q1 *headline:*
- larger than the main text
- at the top of the page
- used to grab attention
subheading:
- larger than the main text
- used to split up a story

Q2 a) • Alliteration is used to make the headline stand out and sound exciting.
b) • A pun is used on the word "pizza" which sounds like "piece of", making the headline amusing.
c) • Emotive words such as "outrage" and "massive" attract the reader's interest by exaggerating the details.

Page 14 — Graphics and Captions

Q1 a) • The purpose of the graph is to inform the reader about population growth. The caption tells you the information the graph shows.
b) • The photo and the caption aim to persuade the reader to stay at the hotel by presenting it in a positive way. The words confirm what the reader sees in the photo.

Q2 Here are some of the points you could include in your answer:
• The heading "MONTSERRAT" is in a very large font, attracting the reader's attention and telling them exactly what is being advertised.
• The subheading, "The Emerald Isle of the Caribbean", creates an impression of Montserrat being mysterious and beautiful, encouraging the reader to read the rest of the advertisement.
• The photographs reinforce the appeal of Montserrat, and suggest that a variety of holiday activities are available.
• The words "idyllic", "secluded", "beautiful" and "unspoilt" in the captions add to the positive impression.

Page 15 — Text Boxes and Columns

Q1 • The columns make it seem easier to read the text by breaking it up and making it seem shorter.

Q2 a) • The text box makes the main point of the article stand out from the details of the text, to appeal more effectively to the reader. The text box itself is an eyecatching shape and makes the offer look exciting and enticing.

b) • The text boxes separate the details of the two children, emphasising that they are individual people with different stories. The boxes make the text easier to read.

Page 16 — Bullet Points and Numbered Lists

Q1 a) • It would be hard to take in all six symptoms if they were listed in a solid piece of text. The bullet points separate the symptoms from each other, so that the information is easier to follow.
b) • The numbered list makes the order of the different stages of the recipe clear, so that it is easy to use.

Page 17 — Font Styles and Formatting

Q1 a) • The font creates a formal impression, to match the serious nature of the subject.
b) • The font gives a light-hearted impression, supporting the idea of having fun.
c) • The font is designed to look like handwriting, to give the impression the the text is informal advice written by a friend.

Q2 a) • Bold text is used to emphasise the most important part, i.e. the size of the pay rise.
b) • Italic text is used to separate the headings from the information about the event, making the information easier to absorb.

Page 18 — Presentation and Layout — Overview

Q1 *There are many points you could make — these include:*
• Bullet points are used to list the different superfoods, presenting the information in small chunks so that it is easy to see where one point ends and another one starts.
• Text columns make the text look shorter by breaking it up into short sections, rather than having one long block of text.
• The advice about taking regular walks is placed in a box, to make the information stand out.
• The informal font style makes the text easy to read, encouraging the reader to carry on with the advice even though it may seem complicated.
• Important words are underlined to make the main points stand out.

Section Four

Page 19 — Descriptive Language

Q1 • Language that describes something by creating a picture, e.g. metaphors and similes.

Q2 a) smell
b) touch

Q3 I had five <u>tedious</u> hours to wait at Singapore's <u>shiny, modern</u> airport. While my <u>bulging</u> holdall rested at my <u>tired, sandalled</u> feet, I observed the <u>curious</u> surroundings. An <u>interesting</u> mix of travellers bustled by: <u>excited</u> families, <u>overweight</u> businessmen, <u>dirty young</u> backpackers. My nostrils detected the <u>heavenly</u> scent of <u>fresh</u> croissants and <u>strong</u> coffee wafting from the <u>over-priced</u> eateries. I felt a <u>slight</u> chill and <u>dry</u> mouth from the air conditioning, yet was grateful: better to be sitting in a <u>fake, cool</u> breeze than wilting outside under the <u>burning</u> sun.

Q4 Here are some points you could make for these two questions:
a) • The writer seems to find the bridge scary — he says it is "ghostly".
• The writer seems fond of the bridge though, as he wants to "take a stroll" there.
• He seems regretful that the bridge is now closed and inaccessible — e.g. "unnecessary barbed wire fence".
b) • Adjectives like "ghostly" and "forbidding" give the impression that the bridge is mysterious and frightening.
• The imagery of "thunderous roar" is effective in bringing home how loud and awesome the trains were.
• The simile "like a warning of an alien invasion" is used to convey a sense of a strange, other-worldly feel to the scene.
• The personification of "thorny bushes which try to trip you up" creates an impression of the bridge now being guarded aggressively and dangerously.

Page 20 — Metaphors and Similes

Q1 a) A comparison where the writer says that something is something else.
b) A comparison where the writer says something is similar to something else, often using the words "like" or "as".

Q2 a) simile
b) metaphor
c) metaphor
d) simile

The Answers

Q3 • It creates the impression that Jane is really embarrassed because she is blushing a deep purple colour.

Q4 • The metaphor creates the impression that Jane wasn't interested in romance until she kissed Brad Depp.

Page 21 — Personification, Alliteration and Onomatopoeia

Q1 a) Alliteration
b) Personification
c) Onomatopoeia

Q2 a) • Personification — expresses the writer's frustration at the computer not working by making it seem like an annoying, unhelpful person.
b) • Onomatopoeia — helps the reader to imagine the sound of the shoes.
c) • Alliteration — emphasises the message to make it more memorable and therefore more persuasive.

Q3 Here are a few points you could make in an answer to this question:
• A metaphor is used ("a maze") to emphasise how confusing the streets are and show how easy it is to get lost in them.
• The simile used to describe the side streets as "like snakes winding across the desert" makes them sound unpredictable, dangerous and exotic.
• The descriptive phrase "strong but irresistible" is vivid because it suggests that the smell of the food was attractive.
• Personification is used to describe the scooters, e.g. "buzzing", "swarm".
• Onomatopoeia helps the reader to imagine the sounds of the vehicles, e.g. "buzzing".

Page 22 — Irony and Sarcasm

Q1 a) • Saying one thing but meaning another.
b) • Language that uses a mocking or nasty tone, and is often ironic.

Q2 • The writer's sarcastic tone in this article makes it clear that she is strongly opposed to extending licensing hours. She is clearly being sarcastic when she suggests that drinkers will just "take up knitting instead" — this idea is deliberately ridiculous and shows that she thinks the scheme is a bad idea.

Q3 Here are a few points you could make in an answer to this question:
• The writer uses irony (e.g. "horrendously complicated") to express the frustration he feels when dealing with call centres.
• The writer seems to dislike the whole call centre process. He describes spending "20 thrilling minutes" listening

to hold music — his ironic tone shows his frustration at how long he had to wait.
• He says that being told there were technical problems was a "great comfort" which is clearly ironic.

Page 23 — Technical and Emotive Language

Q1 a) T
b) E
c) E
d) E

Q2 • Rhetorical questions such as "Do we want them to have fresh air to breathe?" try to influence the way the reader feels about the situation.
• There are exaggerated descriptions of what the world could end up like — "filthy, concrete planet with nothing left" is contrasted with "green and pleasant land", emphasising how important the decisions we make now are.

Q3 • Figures and statistics, e.g. "between 500 and 1000mm," allow the writer to get across clear and precise information.
• Using technical terms such as "insolation" suggests the writer knows a lot about the subject and so can be trusted to be accurate.

Page 24 — Structure

Q1 "separate paragraphs", "opinions", "specific details" and "statistics" should be circled.

Q2 a) The **body** of the article...
• because it gives details that expand on what is in the introduction.
b) The **conclusion**...
• because it summarises the main issue of the article and speculates on what will happen next.
c) The **introduction**...
• because it introduces the topic and outlines the main points of the article.

Section Five

Page 25 — List Questions

Q1 Possible points include:
• The entrance gate is rusty / in need of repair.
• The ground is covered in litter.
• Most of the animals look underfed/ miserable.
• The enclosures are small.
• The animals have nothing to do.
• It's a depressing place.

Q2 Possible phrases include:
• "Hardly any of it's original..."
• "...it's just far too easy to make"
• "rock music involves real instruments that need skilled musicians"
• "hip hop's created... from recycled bits of somebody else's music"

Page 26 — P.E.E.

Q1 Option (c) should be circled.

Q2 Answers (a) and (c) should be ticked.

Q3 Possible answers include:
• *Point:* The writer uses bullet points.
Example: The description of the types of skeleton in each chamber is broken up into bullet points.
Explanation: Bullet points break the information up, making it clearer and easier to read and understand.
• *Point:* The writer has formatted the heading differently from the main text.
Example: The heading "West Kennet Long Barrow" is in bold and a large font size.
Explanation: A large, bold heading stands out, so it is immediately clear what the information sheet is about.

Page 27 — Writing in Paragraphs

Q1 All the words and phrases should be circled apart from: "In the summer" and "The writer says".

Q2 Phrases which have been added to improve the flow of the paragraphs are underlined:
a) • The writer uses several presentational devices to make the article more effective. One example is the headline, which is in a large, bold font. This grabs the reader's attention immediately when he or she sees the article.
Another example is the grey background colour of the article. This emphasises the serious tone of the article. Dull colours like grey are associated with serious subjects.

b) • The writer uses language devices to make her argument more persuasive. Firstly, she uses the rhetorical question "Who would want an axe-murderer living next door?" to encourage the reader to identify with her point of view.
Secondly, the writer uses a metaphor to describe her opinion: "this situation is a slippery eel which might twist out of our grasp". This creates a vivid image of the difficulty of the situation.

The Answers

c) • The first text argues in favour of school uniforms. For example, it describes them as "a symbol of unity and school identity" which implies a traditional, positive viewpoint.

In contrast to this, the second text argues against school uniforms. It describes them as "a fashion disaster" and "an embarrassment to pupils". This suggests a very negative opinion.

d) • The book extract is aimed at an audience of primary school children. It includes simple pictures to explain how to use a camera. This makes it easy for children to understand.

The magazine article, on the other hand, is aimed at adults who are interested in photography. It uses technical vocabulary such as "developer" and "focus" which shows it's written for photography enthusiasts.

Page 28 — Reading with Insight

Q1 a) iv)
b) iii)
c) i)
d) ii)

Q2 a) *Words and phrases which imply the writer dislikes Hitchcock's later films:*
• "slow", "self-satisfied"
Words and phrases which imply the writer likes Hitchcock's early films:
• "enjoyable", "funny"
Words and phrases which imply the writer dislikes Hitchcock as a person:
• "bullying", "large ego"
b) • I really enjoy John Bhasker's crime thrillers. I find them pacy and exciting, yet they always contain wonderful humour and a hidden moral.

Page 29 — Comparing Texts

Q1 a) Possible points to include in the table:
Audience of text:
• Linda's problem page is aimed at young teenage girls.
• The financial advice is aimed at adult readers with some knowledge of financial jargon.
Purpose of text:
• Linda's problem page gives girls advice on personal problems.
• The financial article gives advice to readers in similar financial situations.
Tone of text:
• Linda's problem page has a friendly and chatty tone.
• The financial advice article has a fairly formal, serious tone.

Main language devices used:
• Linda's problem page uses chatty language, e.g. "Don't worry though." It uses contractions ("won't") and slang ("Oops"). The text uses the writer's first name, "Linda".
• The financial article uses fairly formal vocabulary, e.g. "earning", "contributes". It is written in the third person and refers formally to "Ms Cox" rather than using her first name. Technical financial terms and figures are also used.
Main presentational devices used:
• Linda's problem page has a photo of Linda smiling. A text box is used to make the reader's letter stand out. The font is quite informal. There are subheadings in colour.
• The financial article uses a formal font. The details of the case study are in a text box. The text box is grey in colour. Text columns are used.

b) Points you could make include:
• Linda's problem page uses chatty language, for example "Don't worry though", which creates a friendly tone. The financial article however uses much more formal language, for example "earning", "contributes".
• Linda's problem page is written in the first person ("My advice is") and uses first names ("Zoe") which makes the tone seem friendly and caring. The financial advice column is written in the third person ("she's currently losing") and uses formal names ("Ms Cox"). This creates a more serious tone.
• The problem page uses an informal font because it is aimed at young girls and is intended to be fun. In contrast, the financial advice article uses a formal font because it is aimed at adults and is about a serious subject.
• Both texts use boxes to make certain points stand out. The problem page puts the reader's letter in a box. The financial article puts the case study in a box.
• The problem page uses colour to highlight the subheadings and page heading to grab the reader's attention. The financial article on the other hand, is in black and white with a grey text box. This makes the article seem serious.

Section Six

The most important part of marking the sample answers is how you explain the mark you've given. If you've put 1 mark more or less than we've put here, it doesn't matter.

Page 35 — Sample Answers — Question A1

Answer 2: • This answer gets 5 marks out of 10 because it only mentions five points that are relevant to the question. Other points are made, but don't they help to answer the question.

Page 37 — Sample Answers — Question A2

Answer 1: • This answer gets 6 marks out of 10 because it makes several comments about the ways Marc Leverton has made the article interesting. All three bullet points are covered and evidence from the article is used to support the answer. To get a higher mark, points should be explained in more detail.

Answer 2: • This answer gets 2 marks out of 10 because it makes a simple attempt to answer the question. The points lack detail and aren't fully explained. It contains personal opinions that aren't relevant to the question.

Page 39 — Sample Answers — Question A3

Answer 1: • This answer gets 1 mark out of 10 because it doesn't answer the question well. It copies from the text instead of quoting properly and is written in a confusing way.

Answer 2: • This answer gets 9 marks out of 10 because it is detailed and well-organised. It uses a quotation to back up every point and shows good understanding of the text.

Page 41 — Sample Answers — Question A4

Answer 1: • This answer gets 8 marks out of 10 because it makes clear comments on the similarities and differences between the two texts. It is a well-structured answer that covers all four bullet points. Short quotations are used to link back to the article. It would score higher marks if it had a little more detail.

The Answers

Answer 2: • This answer gets 3 marks out of 10 because it answers some parts of the question, but doesn't include much detail. A single quotation from the article is used, but its meaning isn't clear. The final sentence isn't relevant to the question.

Section Seven

Page 42 — Practice Exam Questions

A1   *Here are some points you could make in your answer:*
- You gain new skills.
- You try something different.
- You get involved in your community.
- You meet new people.
- It involves taking dogs out for walks.
- It involves playing with dogs.
- It involves helping dogs to socialise.
- It involves raising money for dogs' welfare.
- The rewards are endless.
- It's the next best thing to owning a pet.
- People help out whenever they can manage it.
- Volunteering is flexible.

A2   *Here are some points you could make in your answer:*
- The headline of the article suggests that you can benefit by volunteering.
- It makes dogs sound appealing by describing them as "delightful" and as animals that "love people visiting them".
- It even suggests that you might find romance, when it says "You might even meet the love of your life!" when out walking a dog.
- The article mentions the health benefits of walking dogs, claiming that they are "a great way to get fit!"
- It has an informal tone, such as when it talks about "15 delightful greyhounds", which makes it feel like someone friendly is talking to you and makes you more likely to agree with them.
- Interviews with current workers make it clear that anyone is welcome — they have volunteers "from all walks of life."
- The article says that "there's likely to be" a branch near you, so it sounds like volunteering would be easy to arrange.
- It directly addresses the reader throughout e.g. "Volunteering is also very good for your health", which makes you feel that the comments directly apply to you.

A3   *Here are some points you could make in your answer:*
- Matthews already wanted a dog and was aware that "greyhounds were in most need of a home", so decided to get one. She also thought that a greyhound would make her look "elegant".
- She picked a greyhound which she thought looked "laidback" and when she got it home it acted like a puppy, taking an interest in reflective surfaces and learning how to climb the stairs. She enjoyed having the greyhound immediately, describing her as "fun from the start."
- She has enjoyed the greyhound because it has brought her "plenty of fresh air and exercise" — meaning that she is more active than she was. But she has found that it takes up quite a lot of her time, saying that she's had to rely on "professional dog walkers, friends and family" so that her greyhound isn't left alone for too long.

A4   *Here are some points you could make in your answer:*
- The purpose of the Retired Greyhound Trust article is to persuade people to volunteer. The purpose of 'The joy of greyhound ownership' is to describe one person's experience of owning a greyhound in an entertaining way.
- Both articles have informal, positive titles that emphasise the "benefit" and "joy" of greyhounds.
- The Retired Greyhound Trust article is one long block, but it has some text in boxes at the side to highlight important points. The BBC News article is separated by subheadings that break-up the text and make it look more approachable.
- The content of the two articles is similar in that both articles suggest that greyhounds make good pets. The Retired Greyhound Trust article says "that once you meet a greyhound at one of our branches it's likely to be love at first sight" and Jenny Matthews describes greyhounds as "gentle and affectionate and absolutely brilliant with children".
- The content of the two articles is different because the Retired Greyhound Trust is trying to persuade people to come and help with the dogs in their care, whereas the Jenny Matthews' article is about the fun you can have actually owning a dog.

WRFA41

ISBN 978 1 84762 107 8

9 781847 621078

WRFA41

Personification, Alliteration and Onomatopoeia

Q1   Fill in the blanks in the following sentences.

a)   .... means repeating the same sound at the start of words in a phrase,
      e.g. "Anthony and Ainsley ate asparagus."

b)   .... means describing something as if it is a person or animal,
      e.g. "The car crept stealthily round the bend in the road."

c)   .... means using words that sound like the thing they are describing,
      e.g. "And then: BOOM! Another explosion."

Q2   For each extract, write down the technique being used and say what effect it creates.

a)   "The computer squawked into life before cheerily informing me that I had
      performed an illegal operation."

      ....

      ....

b)   "Her heels made the same clickety-clickety-click you'd expect from a tap dancer."

      ....

      ....

c)   "Bag a Bargain at Brigson's — Portsmouth's Premier Pig Farm!"

      ....

      ....

Q3   Read the following extract from a travel book then answer the question that follows.   MINI-ESSAY QUESTION

> The streets of Kuala Lumpur are a maze of lost lanes, back-streets, dead-
> ends and confusing alleys which double back on themselves. An
> apparently endless series of side streets breaks out from the main street
> of the Chinatown area like snakes winding across the desert. On every
> corner hang the strong but irresistible smells of food stalls offering an
> abundance* of exotic cuisines.
>
> The low growl of heavy trucks and buzzing of the thousands of scooters
> that swarm the streets like bees made my dreams of a bit of peace and
> quiet ridiculously optimistic. The sticky heat, combined with choking
> exhaust fumes and loud noise certainly made for a lively but less than
> relaxing atmosphere.

* an abundance = a lot

What techniques does the writer of this text use to make his descriptions vivid and effective?

Irony and Sarcasm

Q1 Briefly explain each of the following terms:

a) irony ....

....

b) sarcasm ....

....

Q2 What is the effect of the writer's sarcastic tone in this article about extending pub licensing hours?

> **From *Unhappy Hour* by Jane Green**
>
> Of course, the solution to binge-drinking is perfectly clear: we should keep pubs open all day long. This way, everyone will get bored of the idea of beer and take up knitting instead. I can picture it now: the young louts who terrorise our streets will surely all turn to each other and say, "Do you know what, Jeremy? This drinking lark just isn't the fun it used to be when we got cleared out by 11 — I'm seriously considering my life options".

....

....

....

....

....

....

Q3 How does the writer of the following extract use irony to express his opinion? MINI-ESSAY QUESTION

> **From *Customer Disservice — modern day madness* by Mel Sage**
>
> The other day I had to phone up my insurance company with the horrendously complicated problem of changing my address. After spending 20 thrilling minutes on hold listening to a variety of boy bands performing their hits, I finally got through to the man who could help me — Wayne.
>
> However, there was a slight hitch. Wayne informed me that he was having some "technical problems", which was obviously of great comfort to me, as I watched night-time slowly approach and began to revise my plans for what was left of the week.

Technical and Emotive Language

Q1 For each language feature, fill in the box with a **T** if it's used in technical language or an **E** if it's used in emotive language.

a) statistics ☐

c) strong opinions ☐

b) exaggeration ☐

d) rhetorical questions ☐

Q2 Find two examples of emotive language in the following text, taken from a leaflet published by an environmental group. For each example, describe what effect it creates.

> What kind of future do we want to give our children? Do we want them to have fresh air to breathe? Do we want a clean, safe environment they can enjoy and share with their own children?
>
> Or do we want a filthy, concrete planet with nothing left of our once green and pleasant land, where trees are just something fondly recalled by our grandparents?
>
> The answer is surely obvious. Yet if we allow the situation to carry on as it is now, with mass deforestation and overdevelopment in the world's most fragile environments, we're heading for disaster. We must take action now if we have any hopes of avoiding this catastrophe.

1. ....

....

....

2. ....

....

....

Q3 Why does the writer use technical language in this extract about weather and climate?

> The United Kingdom has a temperate maritime climate, with most lowland areas receiving between 500 and 1000mm of annual rainfall. Annual temperatures are generally between 5 and 15°C, with urban areas up to 5°C warmer than rural areas, due to the urban heat island effect. The south is also warmer than the north, due to higher levels of insolation*.

* Insolation is radiation from the sun that heats the planet.

....

....

....

....

Structure

Q1   Circle the features that you would usually expect to find in the body text of an article.

summary of the main points

separate paragraphs

captions

opinions

headlines

specific details

statistics

Q2   The following extracts have all been taken from the same newspaper article. For each one, say whether you think it is from the introduction, the body of the article, or the conclusion. Explain your answers.

a)

> Many motorists are in favour of the new trial scheme, seeing it as a simple, common-sense solution that will reduce traffic jams. But critics are concerned that, when the hard shoulder is being used for normal traffic, there will no longer be a safe place for broken-down vehicles to await rescue.

....

....

b)

> The main issue is whether this can effectively reduce congestion without adding to accident rates. If it can, it is likely to prove much more popular than other methods, such as toll roads. If the scheme proves successful, it could be introduced to motorways up and down the country.

....

....

c)

> A controversial new scheme to avoid traffic congestion on one of Britain's busiest roads has divided opinion among motorists and road safety groups. The strategy, on trial from this week, allows drivers to use the hard shoulder when the amount of traffic is at its highest.

....

....

Every bit of the article is important

Although they contain less information than the body of the text, the introduction and conclusion are important. The intro gets the readers' interest and the conclusion is what will stick in their minds.

List Questions

Q1   Read the text below.

"Last weekend we found ourselves with nothing to do on a warm, sunny day, so decided on a trip to the zoo. The entrance to the zoo was via a rusty iron gate that looked in serious need of repair. The ground was covered in litter. I thought things might improve once we were inside, but unfortunately I was wrong: the majority of the animals looked malnourished and miserable in their enclosures, which all seemed dull and empty, with nothing for the animals to do and precious little space for them to run around in. All in all, it was a pretty depressing place."

List five things you learn about the zoo that suggest it is badly run.

1. ....

2. ....

3. ....

4. ....

5. ....

Q2   Read the text below.

I just can't understand the popularity of hip hop. Hardly any of it's original, and it's just far too easy to make. Whereas rock music involves real instruments that need skilled musicians, hip hop's created mainly on a computer, and often from recycled bits of somebody else's music. I'm not saying that anyone could do it, but I can't believe it's particularly difficult.

Write down **three phrases** from the text that would help to answer the question: "Why does the writer think that rock music is better than hip hop?"

1. ....

....

2. ....

....

3. ....

....

P.E.E.

Q1 In an exam answer, which of the following should you **never** use as an example to back up a point? Circle the correct answer.

a) A quote from the text.

b) A fact or statistic from the text.

c) Your opinion of the subject of the text.

d) A description of the presentation and layout of the text.

Q2 Read the following exam answers. Tick the answers which use the P.E.E. technique (Point, Example, Explanation).

a) The writer uses similes to make his description of Kidston's motor racing more vivid. For example, he describes Kidston's Bentley as being "like a cheetah". This shows how powerful and fast Kidston's car was.

b) The writer says the racing driver Glen Kidston was glamorous and charming. He had an affair with the young Barbara Cartland. In 1931, he died tragically in a plane crash in the Drakensberg Mountains.

c) The writer uses the headline of the magazine article to capture the reader's attention. It describes Glen Kidston as "Britain's Forgotten Hero". This sounds glamorous and mysterious and would intrigue readers.

☐   ☐   ☐

Q3 Read the following extract from a tourist information sheet and answer the question that follows.

Avebury Visitor Centre: Information Sheet 5

West Kennet Long Barrow

West Kennet Long Barrow is an ancient chambered tomb near Avebury. There are five chambers (rooms) in the tomb. It is safe to go inside the tomb to look at the chambers. When the tomb was excavated, different types of skeleton were found in each chamber:
• Male adult skeletons were found in the main chamber, opposite the entrance.
• Children's skeletons were found in the chamber to the left of the entrance.
• The skeletons of elderly people were found in the chamber to the right of the entrance.
• A mixture of male and female adult skeletons were found in the two other chambers.

Explain how the writer has used a presentational device to make the text more effective. Use the P.E.E. framework below to help you answer the question.

Point ....

....

Example ....

....

Explanation ....

....

....

Writing in Paragraphs

Q1   Circle the words and phrases which would be useful for linking paragraphs together.

Another point of view is   Also   Secondly

Although   The writer says

In addition to this   In the summer

However   On the other hand

Q2   In the following exam answers, the student hasn't linked his paragraphs together well. Rewrite each of the exam answers (a-d), so that the paragraphs are linked smoothly together.

You'll need to write your answers to this question on separate paper.

a)   The writer uses several presentational devices to make the article more effective. One example is the headline, which is in a large, bold font. This grabs the reader's attention immediately when he or she sees the article.
    The background colour of the article is grey. This emphasises the serious tone of the article. Dull colours like grey are associated with serious subjects.

b)   The writer uses language devices to make her argument more persuasive. Firstly, she uses the rhetorical question "Who would want an axe-murderer living next door?" to encourage the reader to identify with her point of view.
    The writer uses a metaphor to describe her opinion: "this situation is a slippery eel which might twist out of our grasp". This creates a vivid image of the difficulty of the situation.

c)   The first text argues in favour of school uniforms. For example, it describes them as "a symbol of unity and school identity" which implies a traditional, positive viewpoint.
    The second text argues against school uniforms. It describes them as "a fashion disaster" and "an embarrassment to pupils". This suggests a very negative opinion.

d)   The book extract is aimed at an audience of primary school children. It includes simple pictures to explain how to use a camera. This makes it easy for children to understand.
    The magazine article is aimed at adults who are interested in photography. It uses technical vocabulary such as "developer" and "focus" which shows it's written for photography enthusiasts.

Link your paragraphs together smoothly...

Learn a few of those <u>handy little phrases</u> for linking paragraphs. They're the kind of thing that examiners look out for — they show you've thought about your writing.

Reading with Insight

Q1   Draw lines to match up each sentence (a-d) with the type of tone it conveys (i-iv).

a) I was disgusted by the badly-researched, shabby journalism displayed by your newspaper's coverage of the event.

i) **light-hearted tone**

b) The MP Gareth Soames visited the County Hospital on Thursday 11th December to open a new ward.

ii) **sarcastic tone**

c) Gary Barlow's dancing drew gasps of wonder from the crowd — the rumours were true, he really had improved!

iii) **serious tone**

d) There's nothing I love more than queueing in a really long traffic jam on a boiling hot day — it's fantastic.

iv) **angry tone**

Q2   Read the following text and answer the questions which follow.

> The films Alfred Hitchcock made in the 1950s and 1960s contain glimpses of greatness. Images from these films have become famous, for example Janet Leigh screaming in the shower in 'Psycho'.
>
> However, when looking at Hitchcock's career as a whole, it is his earlier films from the 1930s and 1940s which are the most enjoyable. Early films like 'The 39 Steps' and 'The Lady Vanishes' are very funny and have a great lightness of touch. In contrast, his later films, even classics like 'Vertigo' and 'The Birds', are often slow and humourless.
>
> One reason for the change in quality of Hitchcock's films was the way he started to be treated as an important, "auteur*" director as he got older. Younger film directors like François Truffaut worshipped him. This swelled Hitchcock's already large ego, and meant his style of film-making became more self-satisfied and dull. Stories from the 1950s and 1960s about his bullying, possessive attitude towards young actresses like Tippi Hedren also raise doubts about his professionalism in his later years.
>
> So my advice is: settle down on the sofa to watch some of those early, off-the-cuff Hitchcock masterpieces — and leave the later "classics" for nerdy film students.
>
> ** auteur = when a director of a film is so important that they are considered to be the author of the film*

a) Pick out words and phrases from the text to complete the table below.

Question 2 take 2

Words and phrases which imply the writer dislikes Hitchcock's later films	Words and phrases which imply the writer likes Hitchcock's early films	Words and phrases which imply the writer dislikes Hitchcock as a person
1.	1.	1.
2.	2.	2.

b) In this text, the writer describes how much he likes Alfred Hitchcock's early films. Briefly describe something you feel similarly enthusiastic about.

....

....

....

....

Comparing Texts

Q1   Read the following two texts and answer the questions which follow.

Linda's Problem Page — answers your most embarrassing problems!!!

I farted in front of him!
Dear Linda,
There's a boy at school I really like. He sat next to me in a Maths lesson and I was really excited cos I thought he might fancy me. But I farted and he hasn't talked to me since. What can I do? Love Zoe xxxxx

Linda says....
Hi Zoe,
Oops! How embarrassing! Don't worry though. Silly moments like this happen to all of us. If this boy really likes you, he won't let one fart get in the way of a relationship. My advice is: be confident, and go and talk to him next time you see him. You'll both soon forget all about it. Good luck! Linda.

Write to Linda c/o 'Girl!' magazine, PO Box 5058

Personal Financial Advice: Case Study

Case Study: Ms Cox, 35, single, no children
Salary: £18,000 per year
Savings: £14,500 in a savings account
Pension: Contributes 8% of her salary to a private pension.
Property: 1 bed flat, mortgage £290/month.
Debt: Credit card debt £2100

The Daily Missive's financial advisor, Greg Smith writes
Ms Cox should pay off her credit card debt using part of her savings. She's likely to be paying more interest on her credit card debt than she is earning on her savings, so she's currently losing money.
Secondly, Ms Cox should find out whether her employer would be prepared to make contributions to her pension, which would improve her pension fund.

a)   Complete the following table with notes about the two texts.

	Linda's Problem Page	Personal Financial Advice
Audience of text		
Purpose of text		
Tone of text		
Main language devices used		
Main presentational devices used		

b)   Compare how each text uses language and presentational devices.   MINI-ESSAY QUESTION

Please leave your message after the sarcastic tone...

You're rattling through the book now — only the exam section left to go. Don't worry about that — it might look like a tiger, but it's really just a harmless tabby cat. Ahh.

Sample Exam — Questions

In this section, you get to be the examiner. You'll look at some students' answers to exam questions and decide what marks they should get. It'll help you understand what examiners are looking for — which will improve the quality of your own answers. Here's how it works:

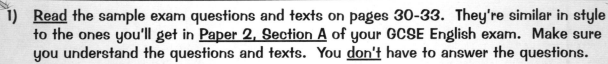

1) Read the sample exam questions and texts on pages 30-33. They're similar in style to the ones you'll get in Paper 2, Section A of your GCSE English exam. Make sure you understand the questions and texts. You don't have to answer the questions.

2) Then on pages 34-41 there are mark schemes explaining how to mark each question. And there are some student answers which you have to mark.

Here are the sample exam questions. Remember — this time, you don't have to answer the questions. Phew.

---

*The **Resource Material for these questions** is an article 'The Recipe for Success' from 'The Big Issue' and an extract from the autobiography of Madhur Jaffrey.*

Look at the article 'The Recipe for Success' from the recruitment section of the magazine 'The Big Issue'

A1 Look at the whole article.

List ten things you learn about chefs at the new Fifteen restaurant in Cornwall, including how they were chosen and how they were trained.   [10 marks]

A2 Look again at the whole article.

How does the writer, Marc Leverton, try to make this an interesting article?
You should consider:
  •   the use of the headline and photograph;
  •   what he tells us about Fifteen that is interesting;
  •   any other ways he tries to make the article interesting.   [10 marks]

Now look at the extract from Madhur Jaffrey's autobiography entitled 'Climbing the Mango trees'.

A3 Look again at the first four paragraphs of the extract.

What impression does Jaffrey give of how food was eaten and prepared in these paragraphs?   [10 marks]

To answer the next question you need to look at both texts.

A4 Compare the article from 'The Big Issue' and the extract from Madhur Jaffrey's autobiography, using these headings:
  •   the purpose of each text;
  •   where the cooking takes place;
  •   the types of caterer or chef mentioned;
  •   the attitudes to food and cooking.   [10 marks]

Sample Exam — Text

Here's the first text to go with the exam questions on p.30. It's an article from the recruitment section of 'The Big Issue'.

Recruit3+

The Big Issue South West and Cymru   May 1 – 7 2006

Recruit 3+ specialises in: local authorities, housing associations, employers in the healthcare sector, charities and other organisations in the voluntary and 'not for profit' sectors.

"Jobs From The Third Sector And Beyond... For those that want to make a difference"

In 2002, TV audiences were transfixed as Jamie Oliver set underprivileged young people to work in his new London eatery, Fifteen. Now the restaurant and its ethos have expanded to Cornwall and a fresh bunch of trainee chefs By Marc Leverton

THE RECIPE FOR SUCCESS

Many people dream of dumping the desk job to work in a beach restaurant but this is now reality for a group of underprivileged young people in Cornwall. May will see the opening of the first Fifteen restaurant outside of London, the location is the spectacular Watergate Bay near Newquay.

The Fifteen Foundation is a charity which exists to inspire disadvantaged young people – unemployed, under-educated, low skilled – and provide them with the skills and experience necessary to create a career in the restaurant and hospitality industry. The idea for the Foundation was born out of Jamie Oliver's Jamie's Kitchen, which was broadcast on Channel 4 in 2002.

More than 300 applications were received from hopefuls at the end of last year and after a tough week of interviews and selection exercises with 150 of the short listed applicants, the 20 final aspiring chefs were chosen.

Trainee Lee Hodge, 20, from Portreath was among them. "I was really pleased and it felt like a new door had been opened and this was my golden opportunity to succeed in life," he says. "I'm so thankful that I've been given this opportunity and I'm really going to work hard to achieve the best possible outcome I can and make my friends and family proud. You only get one life and you've got to take every opportunity."

Before work can start at the restaurant the trainees have had to undergo a 12-week intensive training course at Cornwall College.

"I'm absolutely delighted by the progress and promise shown by the students in such a short space of time," comments Fiona Were, Fifteen Cornwall's training and development chef.

"What's become really evident is that we're working with a group of really bright kids. They're disadvantaged by a variety of social and personal problems which doesn't affect their ability to learn the skills they need to become great chefs."

One of the key objectives of Fifteen Cornwall is to give young people from disadvantaged backgrounds the opportunity to have a fresh start and turn their lives around. This becomes evident when hearing why some of the students applied for this once in a lifetime opportunity. "I applied to Fifteen because I was fed up with doing nothing with my life. I felt like part of the sofa and I needed to feel like I had a reason to get up and go," says 20-year-old Phil Nancholas from Falmouth.

While working towards a NVQ level one in food preparation and cookery, the trainees are learning the skills needed to work in a professional kitchen as well as experiencing new tastes working with ingredients that many had not encountered before. Talking about his favourite part of the course so far and the experience of being a Fifteen Cornwall trainee, Ashley Channon, 20, from Carbis Bay near St Ives said: "I'm enjoying producing amazing food, making some good mates and enjoying what I am doing at work." ∎

Contact Details:

SOUTH WEST RECRUITMENT
Marc Leverton
Tel: 0117 916 6591
email: ads@bigissuesouthwest.co.uk

WELSH RECRUITMENT
Matt Bates
Tel: 029 2025 5672
email: matthew@bigissuecymru.fsnet.co.uk

WELSH RECRUITMENT
Jane Thomas
Tel: 029 2033 7784
email: jane@bigissuecymru.fsnet.co.uk

VOLUNTEERS RECRUITMENT
Emily Fletcher
Tel: 0117 916 6594
email: emily@bigissuesouthwest.co.uk

ADDRESSES

THE BIG ISSUE SOUTH WEST
5 Brunswick Court,
Brunswick Square,
Bristol, BS2 8PE
Telephone: 0117 9166591

THE BIG ISSUE CYMRU
55 Charles Street,
Cardiff, CF10 2GD
Telephone: 029 2025 5672

"specialists in voluntary and not for profit sector recruitment"

Sample Exam — Text

And here's the second text to go with the exam questions on p.30. It's an extract from a non-fiction book by Madhur Jaffrey.

'Climbing the Mango Trees'

by Madhur Jaffrey

Dinners were fairly generous affairs with about forty or more members of the extended family sitting down to venison* kebabs laden with cardamom*, tiny quail* with hints of cinnamon, chickpea shoots stir-fried with green chillies and ginger, and small new potatoes browned with flecks of cumin* and mango powder. **1**

Winter was also the season of weddings. My father was in charge of the caterers and I was his permanent sidekick. In those days caterers had to cook at home and, certainly in our home, they had to cook under family supervision. So a gang of about a dozen caterers would arrive a few days before the wedding and set up their tent under the tamarind* tree. **2**

First, my father would examine all the raw ingredients. Were the spices 'wormy'? Were there broken grains in the basmati rice? Were the cauliflower heads taut and young? **3**

The outward suspicion from one side and obsequious* reassurances from the other were a game each side dutifully played. In reality, we loved these caterers, who were known for the magic in their hands. They could conjure up the lamb meatballs of our erstwhile* Moghul* emperors and the tamarind chutneys of the street with equal ease. One of the few dishes that they alone cooked was cauliflower stems. For one meal they would cook the cauliflower heads. Then they were left with hundreds of coarse central stems. They cleverly slit them into quarters and stir-fried them in giant wok-like *karhais** with sprinklings of cumin, **4**

<u>*Sample Exam — Text*</u>

coriander, chillies, ginger and lots of sour mango powder. All we had to do was place a stem in our mouths, clamp down with our teeth and pull. Just as with artichoke leaves, all the spicy flesh would remain on our tongues as the coarse skin was drawn away and discarded.

Decades later, in New York City, I helped culinary guru* James Beard — my friend and neighbour — teach some of his last classes when he was very ill. One of them was on taste. The students were made to taste nine different types of caviar and a variety of olive oils, and do a blind identification of meats with all their fat removed. Towards the end of the class, this big, frail man confined to a high director's chair asked, 'Do you think there is such a thing as taste memory?'   5

This set me thinking. Once, several of us who had known each other for decades were sitting by a fireplace in France, talking and reading. My American husband, a violinist, was studying the score of Bach's *Chaconne.* 'Can you hear the music as you read it?' a friend asked.   6

It was the same question in another form. When I left India to study in England, I could not cook at all but my palate* had already recorded millions of flavours. From cumin to ginger, they were all in my head, waiting to be called to service.   7

<u>Glossary</u>

venison = meat from a deer
cardamom = a spice, like ginger
quail = a type of bird, like a pheasant
cumin = a salty but sweet spice
tamarind = a fruit that can be used as a spice
obsequious = flattering

erstwhile = former
Moghuls = people of a historic empire that included India
karhai = a type of cooking pan
guru = a wise teacher
palate = sense of taste

Mark Scheme — Question A1

This page gives you <u>advice and a mark scheme</u> for question A1 of the sample exam.
Read this information and digest it. Then you'll be ready to mark the student answers on p.35.

Question A1 asks for a list

1) Answers just need to pick out <u>ten examples</u> from the text.
2) The answers will get 1 mark for <u>each valid point</u>, up to a maximum of <u>10 marks</u>.
3) Answers can be written as <u>bullet points</u> or as a <u>numbered list</u>.
4) For this type of question only, it's fine for answers to be in <u>note form</u>.

Use this table to mark question A1

The table below shows some of the points that could be picked out of the text to answer this
question. Other points are acceptable as long as they're taken from the text.

Number of marks	Possible points
1 mark for each point made, up to a maximum of 10 marks	• The chefs are all disadvantaged young people. • They were previously unemployed. • They are all under-educated and low skilled. • The restaurant received more than 300 applications. • The chefs were chosen after a tough week of interviews and selection exercises. • 150 of the applicants were interviewed. • 20 chefs were chosen in the end. • Lee Hodge is "really pleased" and "thankful". • The chefs went on a 12-week intensive training course at Cornwall College. • They were all really bright. • The chefs work towards NVQ level one in food preparation and cookery. • They're experiencing new tastes. • Ashley Channon is enjoying being a chef and making new friends.

A good mark — like that nice lad from Take That...

These list questions are a good way to bag the first few marks in the exam. Just take your time,
read through the article and find ten points. And don't feel you have to complicate things with
your own opinions or reactions — if you have ten separate points then you'll get ten marks. Easy.

Sample Answers — Question A1

Now it's your turn to be the <u>examiner</u>. This can be <u>tricky</u> but it's really <u>useful</u> if you can do it.

1) Make sure you've read the advice and table on page **34**.
2) Use the table to <u>mark</u> the answers to question A1 below.
3) <u>Explain</u> how you've decided on the marks in the lines below the answers.
4) The <u>first one's been done for you</u> to show you what to do.

Tick each good point in the answer — that's what real examiners do.

A1 Look at the whole article.

List ten things you learn about chefs at the new Fifteen restaurant in Cornwall, including how they were chosen and how they were trained.

[10 marks]

Answer 1

A1   We learn that the chefs are: disadvantaged young people, unemployed, under educated and low skilled. There were 300 applicants and they chose 150 to interview. 20 people got the job. They have to do a twelve week course at Cornwall College. The course is intensive. The course tutor thinks they are really bright kids. They work to NVQ level 1 in food preparation and cookery and they experience new tastes because they use new ingredients.

This answer gets [10] marks out of 10 because .....*it contains ten separate points that help to*.........

....*answer the question.*...

This one is for you to mark...

Answer 2

A1   May sees the opening of the first Fifteen restaurant outside of London. They use disadvantaged people which I think is a good idea because they might not get the chance to be a chef otherwise. 300 applicants wanted to be chefs and only 20 got the job which shows that they were looking only for the best. Lee Hodge is a chef and he is really pleased that he got the job as a chef. They have to do a twelve week course which must be hard because twelve weeks is quite a long time.

This answer gets [ ] marks out of 10 because ....

....

....

....

Mark Scheme — Question A2

Here's advice and a mark scheme for question A2. Read all this info through — then you'll be prepared for marking the sample student answers on the next page.

Use the bullet points to answer Question A2

1) The answer needs to be <u>balanced</u> — it needs to talk about all three of the bullet points in the question to get all the marks.

2) Answers need to <u>explain</u> the effect of the writer's techniques. Simply spotting and describing the techniques won't get high marks.

Look for good points like these when you're marking

<u>The use of the headline and photograph</u>

- The headline, "The Recipe for Success" suggests that the article will tell you how to be successful. This would make readers curious.

- The photograph shows people who look like they are really focused on their job. It suggests that the chefs are passionate about their work — which might make job-seekers want to read the article.

<u>What he tells us about Fifteen that is interesting</u>

- The scheme was started by celebrity chef Jamie Oliver for a television programme, so readers might have already heard about the restaurants and want to know what is happening now.

- It turns lives around for those who work there, which might be an inspiring story for job-seekers reading the article.

<u>Other ways he tries to make the article interesting</u>

- He tries to make the article interesting by including interviews with some of the chefs and with their teacher, who explains how well the students are doing. These add personal interest.

Remember — these are just suggestions.

Mark question A2 like this

Look at the table below to see what an <u>answer needs to be like</u> to gain each mark. Some rows of descriptions are for a <u>range</u> of possible marks (e.g. 2–4 marks). If the answer does <u>everything</u> in the description, and does it well, give it a mark from the top end of the range. If the answer doesn't do everything, but does do <u>some of it</u>, give it a mark from the bottom end of the range.

Mark	Quality of Answer
0 marks	Nothing written that helps to answer the question.
1 mark	Simple comments with no clear links to the question, or some unselective copying from the text.
2–4 marks	Simple comments, mainly written in the student's own words, with some attempt to answer the question. Uses some evidence from the text. May not cover all three bullet points.
5–7 marks	Several clear valid comments made about the article. Evidence from the text is used to support the answer. Some attempt to describe the effect of the writer's techniques.
8–10 marks	Clear commentary on the text showing a good understanding of the different methods that the writer has used to make an interesting article and the effect of these. Details from the text are used to support the answer. All three bullet points are covered.

Sample Answers — Question A2

Now it's time to have a go at marking answers to question A2. Don't be too merciless...

1) Read the mark scheme on page 36.
2) Use the table to <u>mark</u> the answers to question A2 below.
3) Then <u>explain</u> why you gave those marks in the lines below the answers.

It's how you explain your marking that's the important bit.

A2 Look again at the whole article.

How does the writer, Marc Leverton, try to make this an interesting article?

You should consider:
- the use of the headline and photograph;
- what he tells us about Fifteen that is interesting;
- any other ways he tries to make the article interesting.

[10 marks]

Answer 1

A2   The headline is interesting because it says "success" in big letters, which might interest people who want to find out how to be successful. The picture helps because it shows young, underprivileged people enjoying being chefs. The article tells us how the restaurant was shown on a Jamie Oliver television programme and how life has improved for the people who have worked there. Interviews with the chefs also help make the article more appealing to read. One of them says the restaurant is "amazing". There is also an interview with a teacher.

This answer gets [ ] marks out of 10 because ....

....

....

....

....

Answer 2

A2   I don't think the article is very interesting because I am not very interested in cooking. It has a heading, which is big and grabs the reader's attention. It also has a photograph. It tells us that the chefs were all unemployed and were picked through interviews. The writer also tries to make the article interesting by including a contact phone number that you can ring.

This answer gets [ ] marks out of 10 because ....

....

....

....

....

Mark Scheme — Question A3

Hopefully you'll be getting the hang of it by now. Read through the advice and mark scheme on this page, then mark the answers on p.39.

Question A3 is about impressions

1) The question tells you to look at the first four paragraphs — a good answer will only use evidence from these.

2) This question asks about impressions given by the text — a good answer will pick out specific phrases and discuss their effect.

3) You could use P.E.E. (Point, Example, Explanation) for this type of question.

Although he hoped it would become a talking point, Harry's padded poking stick was ignored at the academy — it made no impression whatsoever.

Look for good points like these when you're marking

- Jaffrey says that "Dinners were fairly generous", so it sounds as if there was lots to eat.
- She talks about dinners attended by "about forty or more members of the extended family", so you get the impression that the meals were large social events.
- They ate food like "venison kebabs laden with cardamom" and "tiny quail with hints of cinnamon". This gives the impression that special ingredients were used and the food was carefully prepared.
- The quality of the food must have been important to her father because he "would examine all the raw ingredients" personally.
- She says that "all the spicy flesh would remain on our tongues". This suggests that the food was enjoyable as well as memorable.
- The food was so good that it appeared to come from "magic" in the hands of the caterers.

There are some other points you could make — these are just suggestions.

Mark question A3 like this

Use the table below to find out what kind of answer would get each mark.

Mark	Quality of Answer
0 marks	Nothing written that helps to answer the question.
1 mark	Some simple comments, possibly with unselective copying from the extract. Answer not clearly linked to the question.
2–4 marks	Some relevant comments, but with limited evidence from the text. Includes some basic description of the impressions given by Jaffrey.
5–7 marks	Mostly clear and valid comments about the impressions given by the text, backed up with some evidence from the text.
8–10 marks	Several clear and valid comments about the impressions created by the text showing a good understanding. Well-chosen evidence from the text is used throughout.

Sample Answers — Question A3

More marking for you to do on this page. Remember to write "v.g." on the good answers... joke.

1) Read the mark scheme on page 38.

2) Use the table to <u>mark</u> the answers to question A3 below.

3) Then <u>explain</u> why you gave those marks in the lines below the answers.

> **A3** Look again at the <u>first four paragraphs</u> of the extract.
>
> What impression does Jaffrey give of how food was eaten and prepared in these paragraphs?
>
> [10 marks]

Answer 1

A3 They used to eat a lot of food at weddings. It says all we had to do was place a stem in our mouths, clamp down with our teeth and pull. In those days caterers had to cook at home which was weird.

This answer gets ☐ marks out of 10 because ....

....

....

....

....

Answer 2

A3 At the start of the extract it says "Dinners were fairly generous" and this gives the impression that there was always plenty to eat. I also think that meal times were when the whole family could get together because it says that there were "forty or more members of the extended family" eating together. Later on, Jaffrey says that her father was "in charge of the caterers" for weddings. This gives the impression that he did not trust the caterers. However, it also says that "we loved these caterers" and this makes me think that Jaffrey must have trusted them and liked what they cooked. At the end, she says that the caterers had "magic in their hands" and gives the impression that she found food exciting because children are excited by magic.

This answer gets ☐ marks out of 10 because ....

....

....

....

....

Mark Scheme — Question A4

This is the last question. Read through this page to find out what a good answer needs to be like.

Question A4 asks for a comparison

1) Comparing means looking for <u>differences</u> as well as <u>similarities</u>.
2) Good answers need to cover <u>both</u> texts equally.
3) The <u>bullet points</u> tell you what the examiner is looking for — good answers should cover all of the bullets.

The similarities were obvious.

Look for good points like these when you're marking

<u>Purpose</u>
- 'The Big Issue' article is written to inform and to encourage people who are job-seeking.
- The Madhur Jaffrey extract is written to describe her childhood memories and share an enthusiasm for food in an entertaining way.

<u>Where the cooking takes place</u>
- In the article from 'The Big Issue', the catering takes place in the Fifteen restaurant in Cornwall.
- In the Madhur Jaffrey extract it is happening in her family's home, even though the cooking is done by external caterers.

<u>Types of caterer or chef mentioned</u>
- The chefs in the article from 'The Big Issue' are all disadvantaged young people, learning new skills for the first time. A teacher at Cornwall College is in charge.
- The chefs in the Madhur Jaffrey article are professionals with "magic in their hands" which suggests they are very skilled. Jaffrey's father likes to take overall control of the catering.

<u>Attitudes to food and cooking</u>
- The article from 'The Big Issue' presents cooking as a chance to escape an underprivileged life and to learn a skill while working. One of the new cooks is "enjoying producing amazing food".
- The Madhur Jaffrey extract talks of food as something you learn about at home, as a chance to socialise with the family and as a sort of "magic".

Mark question A4 like this

Mark	Quality of Answer
0 marks	Nothing written that helps to answer the question.
1 mark	Some simple comments, possibly with unselective copying from the article. Answer not clearly linked to the question.
2–4 marks	A simple attempt to answer the question. Uses some evidence from the text. May not cover all the bullet points.
5–7 marks	Some valid comparisons between the texts backed up with some evidence from the texts. Covers all or most of the bullet points.
8–10 marks	Several clear comments about the similarities and differences between the texts. Evidence from the text used to back up most points. Shows good understanding of the texts and covers all the bullet points.

Sample Answers — Question A4

This is your final page of marking. Then everything's back to normal in section 7.

1) Read the mark scheme and advice on page 40.
2) Use the table to <u>mark</u> the answers to question A4 below.
3) Then <u>explain</u> why you gave those marks in the lines below the answers.

> A4 Compare the article from 'The Big Issue' and the extract from Madhur Jaffrey's autobiography, using these headings:
> * the purpose of each text;
> * where the cooking takes place;
> * the types of caterer or chef mentioned;
> * the attitudes to food and cooking.
>
> [10 marks]

Answer 1

A4

   The purpose of the article from 'The Big Issue' is to give information about Fifteen restaurants and to interest people in being a chef. The Madhur Jaffrey extract is different. It is more descriptive and talks about the food they used to eat such as "chickpea shoots stir-fried with green chillies". The article from 'The Big Issue' doesn't describe any food.

   In the Fifteen article, the catering is all happening in college or in a restaurant. This is different from the Madhur Jaffrey article because there all the cooking happens in the home.

   The types of caterer mentioned are also different — in the article they are "unemployed, under-educated and low skilled" but in the Jaffrey article they were really skilled because they had "cleverly" cut up food.

   In both articles, people like food and cooking. Trainee Lee Hodge said he was "really pleased" and Jaffrey says that she "loved these caterers".

This answer gets ☐ marks out of 10 because ....

....

....

....

Answer 2

A4

   The purpose of the article from 'The Big Issue' is to inform but the purpose of the Madhur Jaffrey extract is to describe. In the Jaffrey extract the caterers are in a tent but they are not in the article from 'The Big Issue'.

   In 'The Big Issue', the types of caterers mentioned are different because they are young. In the Jaffrey extract they have "magic" in their hands.

   I think that both of the articles have a positive attitude to food and cooking. I preferred the article from 'The Big Issue' because it is more interesting.

This answer gets ☐ marks out of 10 because ....

....

....

....

Practice Exam — Questions

Here are some practice exam questions for 'Reading non-fiction and media texts'. They're similar in style to the ones you'll get in <u>Paper 2, Section A</u> of your GCSE English exam.

To make it more like the real exam, do <u>all the questions</u> in one go, and give yourself <u>50 minutes</u> to answer them. Try to use everything you've learnt so far about what makes a good exam answer...

---

*The **Resource Material for these questions** is an extract from the website of the Retired Greyhound Trust, 'Volunteering can benefit dogs and you', and an article from the BBC News website, 'The joy of greyhound ownership', written by Jenny Matthews.*

Look at the website article 'Volunteering can benefit dogs and you'.

A1 Look again at the <u>first six paragraphs</u> of the article, up to "...needed and valued".

List ten things that you learn in these paragraphs about being a volunteer for the Retired Greyhound Trust.   [10 marks]

A2 Now look again at the whole article.

How does the article try to persuade you to become a volunteer for the Retired Greyhound Trust?   [10 marks]

Now look at the website article 'The joy of greyhound ownership' by Jenny Matthews.

A3 What are the writer's feelings about owning a greyhound?

You should consider:
 • Jenny Matthews' reasons for getting a greyhound;
 • what her greyhound was like;
 • the good and bad points of owning a greyhound.   [10 marks]

To answer the next question you will need to look at both texts.

A4 Compare the articles 'Volunteering can benefit dogs and you' and 'The joy of greyhound ownership' using the following headings:

 • the purpose of each text;
 • the layout and presentation of each text;
 • how the content of each article is similar;
 • how the content of each article is different.   [10 marks]

Practice Exam — Text

Here's the first text to go with the practice exam questions on page 42. It's an article from a website about the Retired Greyhound Trust.

Volunteering can benefit dogs and you

Are you a dog-lover who wishes you could own a dog, but circumstances dictate you can't fulfil your dream? Do you want to gain new skills, try something different, get more involved in your community, or meet new people? Becoming a volunteer could be the answer you are looking for.

Volunteering for a dog rehoming charity like the Retired Greyhound Trust (RGT) involves activities like taking dogs out for walks, playing with them, helping them learn to socialise, and raising money for their welfare. The rewards are endless, and it's the next best thing to owning a pet.

Many people may believe that volunteering involves a great deal of personal time, but in fact, in the RGT's case, nothing could be further from the truth. Volunteers can help out on an ad hoc basis, whenever they can manage it.

> **Take your pick!**
> As an RGT volunteer, you could:
> • Take the greyhounds for walks
> • Help transport dogs to their new homes
> • Help out with fundraising or community events
> • Spread the word that greyhounds make wonderful pets!

"Volunteering for the RGT is totally flexible," explains Ivor Stocker, Director of the RGT. "We are really grateful for any time that our volunteers can spare, whether it be an hour a week, an hour a month, or just attending the occasional event.

"People can fit their volunteering in and around their normal lives — it never need become a challenge, simply a great thing to do when time allows."

At the RGT, everyone's contribution, no matter what it involves, is needed and valued.

So, what's actually involved in volunteering at the RGT?

"One of the most popular ways to get involved is by volunteering as a dog-walker," explains Amanda Ainsworth, RGT Office Manager. "Other ways in which people help out include conducting home checks, or transporting dogs. Because we don't have our own Trust vehicles, all the help we get in this area is always appreciated."

The RGT's Sheffield branch, whose kennels are based in nearby Barnsley, cares for around 15 delightful greyhounds at any one time, who all need to be taken for walks like any other dogs.

"For those dog-lovers who can't provide a home for a greyhound, becoming a volunteer greyhound-walker is the best alternative!" says Chairman of the Sheffield branch, John Carter.

> **Become an RGT volunteer!**
> You could:
> • Improve your well-being, health and fitness
> • Meet new people
> • Learn some new skills
> • Increase your employment prospects!

"The dogs just love people visiting them and taking them out and about," John explains. "When out on a walk, greyhounds get the chance to meet other dogs and people, which helps them greatly in learning to socialise. They also get the chance to explore the world beyond the familiarity of their kennels."

Volunteers at the RGT also have wonderful opportunities to meet new people and make friends. "You might even meet the love of your life!" says Director of the RGT, Ivor Stocker, "People out walking their dogs often chat to each other, having a dog by your side is a great ice-breaker."

Volunteering is also very good for your health. It is well-recognised that helping out a worthy cause carries with it a 'feel-good factor', which lifts spirits and gives a heightened sense of well-being. Walking the dogs is also a great way to get fit!

So, what types of people can volunteer to work with retired greyhounds?

"The short answer is — anyone and everyone!" says Amanda Ainsworth. "We have volunteers working with us from all walks of life. Young people through to the elderly — individuals, couples, groups of friends, and of course families can volunteer." Greyhounds are not selective, they love meeting and getting attention from any new friend!

"Beware however," warns Ivor Stocker, "that once you meet a greyhound at one of our branches it's likely to be love at first sight, and you won't want to leave!"

The Retired Greyhound Trust has 75 branches around the UK, so there's likely to be one near you. The RGT is a national charity dedicated to finding homes for former racing greyhounds. Almost 40,000 ex-racing greyhounds have been adopted successfully by all sorts of people, including families and retirees. Contact the RGT's national office on 0844 826 8424 to find out more about volunteering at your local branch. For more information on the RGT and retired greyhounds as pets, log on to: www.retiredgreyhounds.co.uk

Practice Exam — Text

Here's the second text to go with the practice exam questions on page 42.
It's an article from the BBC News website.

The joy of greyhound ownership

By Jenny Matthews
BBC News

One of the sad things about claims that thousands of retired racing greyhounds are being shot dead every year — if true — is that they make excellent pets.

I can't remember why we decided to adopt a retired racing greyhound — I think it was because we wanted a dog and had a vague idea that retired greyhounds were in most need of a home.

It might also have been that a friend told me I would look more elegant walking a greyhound than any other type of dog.

Whatever the reason, about two years ago we found ourselves driving to our nearest retired greyhounds' home in Hersham, Surrey. As we were novice owners, we decided we would choose a quiet dog, to get us in the swing. After inspecting all the different kennels we plumped for a laidback-looking black bitch, called Chrissie (racing name Mulla Pride, they told us; previously a sprinter at Reading; "terrible with cats").

Advice from the home

Racing greyhounds lead very sheltered lives, and in some ways it was like having a new puppy. The reflective surfaces of the sitting-room fireplace fascinated her. She skittered all over the wooden laminate floors. It took her several weeks to learn to climb the stairs.

It was fun from the start.

Many people assume greyhounds need loads of exercise — but because they are built for speed, not stamina, that is not actually true.

Gentle and affectionate

Experts say retired greyhounds need only two 20-minute walks a day. Chrissie would probably happily be out all day if she could, and usually gets about two hours a day, but it's a relief to know we're not doing her any harm if that's all she gets.

They are loyal, gentle and affectionate and absolutely brilliant with children (although many ex-racers are not so good with cats. Or, indeed, squirrels).

Roo

And ever since then, she has brought us enormous pleasure. She makes us get plenty of fresh air and exercise. We have got to know other dog walkers and made many friends. She is good company.

And there are surely fewer happier sights than a previously homeless hound sprawled, legs aloft, on her favourite duvet — or many better sounds that the delighted "roo" of a greyhound who knows she is just about to go out for a walk.

It hasn't all been a breeze. Greyhounds shouldn't be left alone for too long and the responsibility of daily dogcare for an urban childless couple came as quite a shock — if we didn't have professional dog walkers, friends and family to rely on I'm not sure what we would do.

And of course, there have been a few unexpected costs — like replacing the slippery laminate with expensive stone, and seriously considering moving house "for a bigger garden for the dog".

And probably the biggest drawback, as my colleagues will attest — is that they are indeed addictive, and I have become a total greyhound bore.